SINS OF THE GRANDFATHER

THE LITTLE GIRL IN THE BLUE DRESS

SINS OF THE GRANDFATHER

THE LITTLE GIRL IN THE BLUE DRESS

BY

BRUNA SLAVA

www.bookstandpublishing.com

Published by
Bookstand Publishing
Morgan Hill, CA 95037
3306_4

ISBN 978-1-58909-889-3

Printed in the United States of America

Table of Contents

1

THE MAN WITH THE YELLOW FINGERS

Awakened in abject fear from one of her two recurring nightmares, Claire Marie wondered if she was The Little Girl In The Blue Dress. *It must be me*, she thought. *If only I could remember everything.* The more she tried to remember, the queasier her stomach became. Running into the bathroom, she threw up into the toilet bowl as usual. After she cleaned her face with a cold, wet washcloth and rinsed her mouth, she walked back to her bedroom and sat in the rocking chair next to her bed.

Summoning all of her resolve, she forced herself to recall the sickening dream, which she had long ago named "The Little Girl In The Blue Dress Nightmare." This is what thirty-five-year-old Claire Marie remembered about the nightmare:

On the steps in an enclosed outside hallway, Claire Marie saw a little girl wearing a blue dress, white shoes, and socks. The little girl was shivering, even though it was a warm, sunny day. The little girl was alone, wondering where everyone else had gone. It seemed to her as if she was the only person left in the world — except for the man with the yellow fingers.

The little girl in the nightmare knew exactly what was going to happen next, and she shivered again as she balanced herself against the wall as best she could, with one hand against the wall for support. She could not reach the handrail.

Yellow Fingers popped his head into the hall from the basement, and then launched himself without any effort up the steps to where she was standing. She smelled his stench even before he reached her. He reeked of stale beer, gasoline, and cigarettes.

In the nightmare, Claire Marie remembered seeing the little girl wobble a bit as a wave of nausea rippled through her body. Mercifully, the little girl took her mind someplace else when she became overwhelmed with fright.[1] The little girl wished that the hall telephone would ring and that another adult would answer it and save her. But her wish was in vain. She even envisioned the black

---

[1] Dissociative Identity Disorder (DID), which has been known as multiple personality disorder, is the most famous of the dissociative disorders. An individual suffering from DID has more than one distinct identity or personality state that surfaces in the individual on a recurring basis. This disorder is also marked by differences in memory which vary with the individual's alters, or other personalities. Psyweb.com, Mental Illness DSM, 4/22/2008, 9:25 AM.

telephone with the earpiece hanging on the part of the phone next to where people talked. The scratch pad on which the talkers scribbled while they spoke was there, too.

She wished she were someone else. She wished the steps would open up and swallow her.

Yellow Fingers put one rough, sweaty hand on her little leg, and began moving it upwards towards her panties. With his other hand, he pushed her legs apart. At the same time, Yellow Fingers forcefully whispered to the little girl, with his stinking breath, that this was their secret — "The Secret" — and that she could never tell anyone or else she would get into **BIG** trouble.

As soon as his sandpaper hand reached her panties, **whoosh** — the little girl's mind fled the steps.

Claire Marie would then awaken terrified and afraid that Yellow Fingers would come into the room where she lay frightened and shivering. In this recurring nightmare, The Little Girl In The Blue Dress appeared to be about four years old. This nightmare periodically haunted Claire Marie until she was thirty-six years old.

As she sat in the rocking chair, Claire Marie began to cry quietly, wishing and praying that she could remember everything and understand what the dream symbolized. She was thankful that at least Robert, her husband, wasn't at home to see her so shaken.

As bad as that nightmare was, at times a second, even more horrific nightmare would assault Claire Marie without any warning. This nightmare often happened after she had experienced the tart smell of gasoline, or someone's rotten cigarette breath, during the course of her regular day. She had long ago dubbed it "The Purple Mountain Nightmare," but did not know why.

In this repulsive dream, she could not clearly see everything that was happening, but she knew it was happening to the same little girl, The Little Girl In The Blue Dress, who existed in the other nightmare. At least a million times Claire Marie had wondered what it was that was blocking her view. She knew intuitively that there were two others with her in the nightmare. Sometimes she believed that there were a child and an adult; and other times, she believed there were two adults, one of whom was always Yellow Fingers.

Even more confusing was that this nightmare took place on a kitchen table. In the nightmare, it would become almost impossible for her to breathe, and she would awaken drenched in sweat, panicky, and believing she would die on the spot.

4

This nightmare literally brutalized Claire Marie. If she could only figure out what was blocking her view in the dream. She wanted to know, but at the same time feared finding out. The answer would only be revealed to her when she was thirty-six.

In addition, from 1965, when she was twenty-six, up until 1975, when she was thirty-six, Claire Marie would, almost nightly, experience the same recurring hallucination after she had been asleep at night for about two or three hours. Each night before she went to bed, she always told herself that she simply could not possibly stand experiencing the hallucination again, the hallucination she dubbed "The Tarantula Delusion." But she did experience it — again, and again, and again.

Eventually, she learned to expect it. When she awoke she would open her eyes, and, hanging from the ceiling would be fifteen or twenty huge, black, furry tarantulas suspended from the ceiling by long black cords of different lengths. Some of the tarantulas were huge, while others were smaller, the latter ones hanging at different levels from the huge ones. She knew they were not there, not real, as she lifted her hand to touch them. Her hand would simply pass through the imaginary tarantulas, touching nothing.

Once "The Tarantula Delusion" was over, she would lay terrified, and fear would continue to well up inside her. The nausea would mount and her heart would race; and, in the pit of her stomach, she feared that Yellow Fingers might appear.

She could not easily shake her terror. Fear would make her stomach muscles twist inside until the spasms drained her of energy. She always tried to calm herself, and would always try to go back to sleep.

She always found herself unable to articulate the words that would reveal what she knew about "The Secret," even though she had tried hard to do so. The words would travel from her mind into her throat, and then to her mouth, and then turn into dryness, and they would never come out. There were few days in her life during which "The Secret" failed to haunt her. Claire Marie kept silent about what she knew, until someone needed her help.

Having become highly adept at mentally removing herself from situations she feared, or situations that made her feel unsafe and uncomfortable — escaping to what she called her "Safe Place" — Claire Marie could barely remember all of the times Yellow Fingers had been present. At age six, her mental "safety valve" began to cause her problems because she would lose even ordinary memories.

6

Her mother demanded to know why she could not recall specific events, but little Claire Marie had no answer and was mute on the subject.

In 1945, when she was six, she began having difficulties attending family parties where Yellow Fingers lived. Even worse than going to family parties was having Yellow Fingers and her grandmother baby-sit for her and her siblings. She tried crying and throwing tantrums, but could give no logical explanation to her mother or her father as to why she did not want to attend family parties, or why she did not want her grandparents to babysit.

Her fear lived and thrived inside her daily, but she was unable to enlighten anyone about her secret, about "The Secret." For a time, in the first grade, she tried to get out of going to school by feigning illness; but neither her mother nor her father could detect in her any sign of a fever, a cold, or any other childhood disease.

Going mentally to her "Safe Place" was easy for her to do, even when she thought about Yellow Fingers, but she also learned it was often difficult to return to reality. By some means (perhaps by the grace of God), she learned not to retreat into her "Safe Place" unless Yellow Fingers was alone with her. Straddling the two worlds was not easy for her.

2

THE SECRET

"You god damned sick son-of-a-bitch!" shouted the little girl's father. "How could you? She's a little girl — your own flesh and blood — your granddaughter! What kind of an animal are you? I look out the window to see that the kids are okay in the back yard, and what do I see? My own father sitting on the bench with my six-year-old on one knee, and the neighbor's little girl on the other knee. And what are you doing with your hands? Are you nuts? God help you! What in God's name made you do such a thing? How do I explain it to the neighbors? Should I even try to explain it to the neighbors? If I ever catch you near her again, I'll **kill** you! Do you hear me? Don't stand there like some freak! Say it! Say it! Swear to me you will never do this again! You come here to visit and look what's happened! Why? Get out of here! Go prey on someone your own age! Do you hear me? But before you go, remember this: From now on I will be watching you every moment. Now leave my house! Get the fuck out of here!"

"I don't know what got into me. I've never done anything like this before and I won't do it again, I swear. Trust me," said Yellow Fingers as he walked out the door.

"How do we handle this?" sputtered the little girl's mother. "God help us. He's your father. Did you know he was like this? We have to keep him away from our kids. We have to be vigilant. She's only six, just a little girl. Maybe she won't remember. He should be locked up someplace. Who can help us? What do we do? Who would believe us?" she cried between the tears, her voice cracking. "He's a god damned monster!"

"I don't know what to do!" he moaned. "You heard him; he said he never did anything like this before. I don't know if I should believe him. What if he's lying? My own father is a fucking pervert!"

"Who do we tell? Will anyone believe us? How do we know he hasn't done this before? What about the neighbor girl? How can we possibly explain something like this? Should we even try to? I hate the son-of-a-bitch monster! I hate him! I hate him! I hate him! Maybe we shouldn't tell anyone. Maybe we should keep it a secret. Maybe we should wait and see if the neighbors come to us. Then what? God Almighty! Your father is a bastard! I hate him! I hate him! One thing I know for sure: He can't be left alone with kids ever again." The voice and the body of the little girl's mother were shaking so violently that she had to sit down before she fell down.

So, six-year-old Claire Marie was going to be protected by the watchful eyes of her vigilant parents beginning in 1945. What they didn't know was that Yellow Fingers had already molested her countless times.

It had been an especially good time for Yellow Fingers shortly after Claire Marie's birth, because the young family was forced to live with Ma and Pa, as Yellow Fingers and his wife were called by the family, for about six months. The place where the young couple had lived before their baby was born did not allow children. Forced to find a new place to live, they had turned to Claire Marie's paternal grandparents until they located a reasonably priced flat.

Preying on little girls came easy to Yellow Fingers. Oh, how he loved little girls! The younger they were, the better. He would "pleasure" himself with a beautiful little girl whenever the opportunity arose, or whenever he could arrange to be alone with a little girl. He found it easy to get time alone with them, especially at family parties when the adults were otherwise occupied in gabbing, arguing, or bragging. If beer was served at the party — well, that made it even better for him. One too many beers made the partygoers lose even more of their focus.

Babysitting afforded him good molesting opportunities as well. However, this was a bit more problematic because sometimes he would be surprised when the parents returned home early.

Most of all, Yellow Fingers liked beautiful little girls who were too young to get away from him, such as his two little granddaughters. He just *loved* being the grandfather of beautiful little girls, loved to "pleasure" himself with them.

A long time ago (only God knows when), he decided that if he were ever caught in the act, he would pretend as if he had done nothing. If that failed, he would say that he was sorry, and that he had never done anything like it before. Thinking along these lines, he would always smile to himself. After all, he thought, who would believe outrageous stories told by parents or beautiful but stupid little girls?

Furthermore, he knew that most adults were afraid, or ashamed, or too embarrassed to tell anyone else about his "pleasuring" activities. Their stories would simply sound too preposterous to possibly be true.

He recalled when his own daughters were little. He was proud of how he had made them afraid to tell anyone about his acts; and he was also proud of how he had groomed them for specific acts he enjoyed.

To entice them, he would sometimes give the older girls his deputy sheriff's badge as a reward. They were too young to realize the badge was a fake. Besides, he had many deputy badges. Befuddled and very upset and angry when a little girl would refuse his deputy badge, he would force the issue, and enlist his "Special Helper" — the nickname he gave to "It." Sometimes, he would make another child watch what he did; he liked that a lot.

In 1946, when Claire Marie was seven and in second grade at a local Catholic school, the Sister teaching her class taught her and her classmates about the Age of Reason from the time school began in September until their First Holy Communion in May. The Sister explained to the class that at seven years old, they were old enough to be able to discern right from wrong. She cited examples of right and wrong; but never was an example presented even remotely close to Yellow Fingers' acts that Claire Marie could remember.

The Sister did say that when a person does something wrong, they usually know it is wrong, and that when they do it, they feel bad or guilty about it.

She also taught them about the Sacrament of Confession. This meant that one would confess his or her sins in private to a priest, who would give them absolution or forgiveness. Then, one would be able to receive the Eucharist with a spotless soul.

A firestorm raged in the little girl's mind because Yellow Fingers made her feel sick and afraid. If only she could understand what he made her do or exactly what he did. All she knew for sure was that she often got sick to her stomach and threw up when she thought about him. She tried, without success, to figure out what was happening to her whenever Yellow Fingers cornered her. Because she was forbidden to tell anyone about "The Secret," she alone had to determine whether it was right or wrong, and whether it was her fault.

Although she was too young to fully comprehend what Yellow Fingers was doing to her, she strongly sensed that it was wrong, very wrong. Claire Marie agonized over this secret. She figured out that she tolerated Yellow Fingers' presence out of fear.

As a result of the Sister's teachings, Claire Marie gained a newfound responsibility of discriminating between right and wrong. This forced her to ask herself questions that had never before entered her mind. She questioned whether all grandfathers did what Yellow Fingers did (whatever it was) to their granddaughters. Was she the only one harboring "The Secret"? She also wondered why she was supposed to keep it a secret in the first place.

Merely thinking about Yellow Fingers made her heart pound and her mouth dry, and she would try not to throw up. It made her feel so awful and afraid that she wanted to go to her Safe Place. She was puzzled as to why such awful feelings would take hold of her mind and body. She could not explain to herself why she could do nothing about it.

From September to May, she wondered endlessly why Yellow Fingers made sure they were alone when he talked to her about keeping his secret. Slowly, Claire Marie began to understand that she never felt happy around him or about what he did. She was confused about what he did, because she would become so traumatized that she couldn't remember everything. Realizing that she would often feel a wave of nausea when she thought about Yellow Fingers or when he came too near to her, she was compelled to ask

15

herself why she felt sick, afraid, and alone whenever Yellow Fingers came near her.

Claire Marie also thought about the comfort, warmth, and safety she experienced when her mother talked to her, or held her close, or tenderly stroked her face or her hair. Her mother never asked her to keep any of that a secret.

Her father tended to be distant, but she would not understand this until much later. He showed his affection for her by gently stroking one side of her face with the back of his hand. Her father never asked her to keep this a secret either. She never felt afraid or sick when her father showed his affection.

Furthermore, she was extremely confused as to why no one else seemed to notice that Yellow Fingers actually did have yellow fingers. Surely, she thought, everyone should have been able to easily see his hands, and know that he had been touching her panties by the color of his fingers. The little girl simply could not fathom why no one else noticed. She obsessed about Yellow Fingers always demanding that she never tell anyone.

This obsession so occupied and distracted her mind that at school she had a difficult time learning how to correctly write from one to one hundred on a piece of paper. As a result, she was the only pupil whom the Sister ordered to stand in front of the class and count from one to one hundred. For a split second, the little girl almost fled to her "Safe Place"; instead, however, she mustered up her strength and counted aloud from one to one hundred correctly.

But the ordeal wasn't over. Next, the Sister made her sit down in the front desk, in the middle row, and commanded her to write what she had just recited. Somehow, she did it correctly.

At the end of April, the little girl made the decision not to confess her secret to the priest. Her decision was Herculean, because when necessary, the little girl now contrived ways to stay away from Yellow Fingers, even at family gatherings. She would mingle with the adults; and, if they went somewhere else, she went along with them. In effect, she worked hard at never being alone in the same room with Yellow Fingers.

Noticing this he asked her, right in front of the rest of the family, "Don't you like Grandpa anymore?" She didn't respond, and walked away quickly.

Nevertheless, somehow, Yellow Fingers managed to find ways to ensnare her, and the unthinkable would happen yet again. Still, she could not find her voice to tell anyone, to disclose "The Secret."

With her newfound power, however, Claire Marie didn't give up her efforts to avoid Yellow Fingers. In fact, she redoubled her efforts to do what Yellow Fingers despised most of all — deprive him of the opportunity to get her alone. To this end, she found ways to stay away from family parties. Acquiring a girlfriend became an advantage, because her mother would often permit her to play at her friend's home rather than going to her grandparents' home.

By the time Claire Marie reached eight years of age, the little girl's family had grown to include four younger siblings — two brothers and two sisters. As the eldest, she was permitted to babysit them for short periods, which eliminated Yellow Fingers as a casual caregiver. This was a monumental accomplishment for her.

When Claire Marie was nine years old, she began formulating a plan to rid herself forever of Yellow Fingers, or so she thought. Telling "The Secret" was still not an option, but it became increasingly obvious that Yellow Fingers did not like attention being focused on him, especially if he was alone with her. She tried but failed, at first, to make a scene when he got close to her. Claire

Marie thought obsessively about his cleverness at trapping her when she was alone, and vowed to find the perfect opportunity to make her voice heard. She thus made the decision to make her voice heard regardless of the consequences.

At ten years of age, Claire Marie's opportunity finally arrived. The occasion was the 50th anniversary of her paternal grandparents. Many people attended the event. There were people in the enclosed hall, kitchen, dining room, living room, porch, and basement. The living room and dining room were adjacent to one another. Claire Marie was milling around in the dining room among the partygoers.

She began making her way into the living room when Yellow Fingers entered the living room from the porch. Seeing him, she turned to go back into the dining room, but she was not quick enough, and Yellow Fingers grabbed her arm and tried to pull her close to him. Claire Marie's little voice told Yellow Fingers, "If you ever touch me again or even come too close to me again, I will shout to everyone what you do to me."

He tried to pull her a little closer, but she noticeably and convincingly yanked her arm from his hand to get away. "I mean it," she said. "Never touch me again." No one else heard Claire Marie's defiant statement. She believed she had shouted, but in reality her little voice was not loud enough for anyone but Yellow Fingers to hear. But that was enough. Defeated, he skulked into the dining room.

After that momentous day, Yellow Fingers was no longer a physical threat to Claire Marie. She was pleased with herself, and genuinely happy about what she had accomplished. What she failed to understand, however, was that she was stuffing and pushing "The Secret" deeper and deeper into her psyche. At that point, she had no understanding or realization that Yellow Fingers had already damaged her psyche, and that he would continue to do so.

She still thought about what had happened, what he had done to her, usually precipitated by one of the two nightmares. She wondered what the nightmares meant. She couldn't understand what "The Purple Mountain Nightmare" represented. She tried to remember everything in the nightmares after she awoke, but she just never could. What she did know for certain was that the nightmares made her physically sick. She often wondered how she could reveal her secret if she couldn't remember everything. Her prime concern was who would believe her if she ultimately did reveal "The Secret." Without comprehension, each time she decided not to reveal what she knew about "The Secret," she pushed, she stuffed, she pounded, and she buried "The Secret" ever deeper.

For quite a while, though, Claire Marie's life appeared normal. She had good friends in elementary school. Without knowing it, she began a new practice of being perfect. Not wanting anyone to find her making mistakes in her school world, in her friends' world, or in her family's world, she most often did almost everything assigned to her more than once. She usually did school assignments twice, or until she was confident they were perfect.

She also carefully reviewed in her mind instructions from her parents, and she did whatever she was told to do, making doubly sure that what she did was correct. Of course, because she was so "good," her family came to expect much from her. Although her siblings took to referring to her as "goody-two-shoes," her mother was pleased with her dependability.

During this period, Claire Marie's mother experienced life-threatening health problems, and as a result was routinely hospitalized. It was a standing joke in the family that her mother had paid for the newest wing at the local hospital because she spent so much time there.

This situation led to even more responsibility for Claire Marie. She was expected to help not only with babysitting her siblings, but also with other tasks, including walking to the grocery store to fill her mother's shopping lists.

During the summer months when school was out, Claire Marie would take a cold, fresh lunch that her mother had prepared to her father at work. Taking the lunch, she would walk to the bus stop a few blocks away from home, take the first bus, then transfer to another bus, and finally walk to the hot factory where her father worked. To demonstrate his appreciation for the cool, fresh lunch, he would always stroke one side of her face with the back of his hand and gently say, "Thank you, Sis." He always called her Sis.

3

ON BECOMING A PERSON

In junior high and high school, Claire Marie was not infatuated with boys her age. Rather, she and they were merely good friends. In high school algebra class, she and two boys would trade off doing their homework. Having to do algebra only every third day gave Claire Marie more time to spend reading books, a pastime she enjoyed. Her grades in high school were excellent, and she graduated among the top ten in her class. She also made some lifelong friends during high school.

After high school, Claire Marie worked in federal civil service, and was very good at her job. At age nineteen she married, and began helping to put her husband, Robert, through college.

As the years passed by, the babies came, five of them eventually, but she still continued helping Robert with college.

Each morning, she arose two hours before anyone else, dressed for work, prepared breakfast, dressed the little ones, packed up what was needed for the day, put the little ones in the car, took her hubby to the train, dropped the little ones off at the sitter, picked up four carpool riders, and finally drove to work.

After working all day, she would go through the process in reverse, and then prepare supper. In between supper, and playing with or reading to the children, she would manage to do a few loads of laundry. Often she read before going to bed. If Robert needed her to review or edit his schoolwork, she would do so, making the necessary corrections, and then typing his papers.

Helping her hubby with schoolwork had a positive benefit for her. He was majoring in Psychology, and this afforded Claire Marie the opportunity to read all of his psychology books; and, through his many years of schooling, there were many psychology books to read.

Despite all that she learned about psychology from her reading, however, she still could not bring herself to reveal her secret, even though she realized deep down in her psyche that she needed to do so. The most helpful of all of the psychology books came into her hands while Robert was in graduate school: *On Becoming a Person*, by Rogers. This work gave Claire Marie valuable and revealing insights that she needed in order to become a whole person.

4

DIAMOND EARRINGS

After Robert earned his Psychology degree, he entered graduate school and began working towards an MBA. During the period Robert was attending graduate school, problems began seeping into Claire Marie's life. She knew with certainty that her hubby had a girlfriend on the side. In fact, over a period of eighteen months, she documented his telephone calls to the woman, and even saw them together more than once at times when he said he would be elsewhere. In fact, they were so involved with each other that when she spotted them together in a restaurant near the university, they never even noticed her presence. Seeing them together made her shake and feel inadequate.

However, she didn't confront them on that occasion. Instead, she decided she would take a more subtle approach in dealing with the situation, beginning with accumulating evidence of Robert's affair.

To this end, Claire Marie found it easy enough to look at the telephone bills and memorize "her" telephone number. Whenever Claire Marie would have the gut feeling that something was going on, or when her hubby made notes on his calendar showing "away," she would take off work, drive to Chicago, find a place to park, and go to the university.

She had managed to learn both Robert's locker number and his locker combination, although this had not been an easy task. Bravely, she would enter the university, proceed to his locker, open it, and look inside. The first time she did so, she shook all over so fiercely that she could barely get the combination right, and had to redo the combination several times before the locker opened. As soon as she had looked inside she found, much to her sorrow, love notes from the woman to her hubby, a woman's scarf and gloves, and a needle and two spools of thread.

Finally, she confronted Robert. No matter what Claire Marie said about Robert's "friend" to her spouse, however, Robert swore up and down to her that they were nothing more than "friends." Finally he said, "You just don't understand." This made Dorothy Parker's poem *Social Note* shriek loudly in her head over and over again. Every time she heard the poem scream in her head, it gave her a headache. Wanting the shrieking to stop, she came to wish that Dorothy Parker had never written the poem.

26

Social Note

By Dorothy Parker

Lady, lady, should you meet
One whose ways are all discreet,
One who murmurs that his wife
Is the lodestar of his life,
One who keeps assuring you
That he never was untrue,
Never loved another one...
Lady, lady better run!

By the time Claire Marie was thirty-one years old, she had five kids; had only a high school diploma; and had invested all of her time, energy, and love into trying to bring about the dream of a wonderful life together that she and Robert had once shared. If Robert and the woman *were* only friends, then why was the woman never a guest in their home? If they *were* only friends, then why did her hubby's shirts sometimes have make-up on them when he returned home? If they *were* only friends, then why did he send "her" cards and letters that he would hide before sending them? *Maybe he no longer loves me*, Claire Marie thought.

The truly piercing stab came when Claire Marie discovered that Robert had bought his "friend" diamond earrings. This slashed Claire Marie to the marrow of her bones, not only because she had long dreamed of owning a pair of diamond earrings herself, but also because Robert would pacify her by telling her that as soon as they could afford it, when he was out of school, big diamond earrings would be hers. In fact, they had a little joke about the earrings. She would laugh and say that if he took too much longer to graduate and become employed, she might be too old to hold her head up once she had the earrings.

Claire Marie had physical proof, in the form of their credit card bill, that Robert had purchased the diamond earrings for his "friend." *How stupid can the man be?* she thought. *After all, the sale was itemized on the credit card bill. He pays the bills. But does he really believe I'm too stupid to snoop?* Taking the bill, she carefully hid it in her sanitary napkins box under the bathroom sink.

She asked herself over and over again why Robert had not introduced his "friend" to her. Did he see her as so naïve and trusting that he was confident she would not challenge him on the relationship, or, in addition, that she would not snoop to find out the truth?

The gravest question of all that she asked herself was, *Will I be dumped after all I have invested to put him through school?* She knew in her heart of hearts that such was a strong possibility, one that loomed ever larger on the horizon.

Once again, as she had done as a child to resolve the threat of Yellow Fingers, Claire Marie decided that she would solve the problem on her own. One long weekend after Robert returned home from working on his thesis (or so he said), she pointedly informed her hubby that if his affair did not cease, she would disappear without warning, and leave him with all of the "fun" she had experienced in the past several years. She would leave with him the five kids, the bills, and all of the responsibilities; and she would begin a new life on her own. She yelled that she knew she would have no problem getting a good job with good pay. After all, she had supported their family for a long time.

In response, however, he merely laughed at her, and settled into his routine at home. Stung that he had failed to take her seriously, she knew she had to do something to garner his attention.

To this end, Claire Marie devised a plan. She knew she had to be careful with her plan because hurting her children in any way was totally out of the question. Making

29

her husband understand that his only choice would have to be her and their children became her purpose. She would have to make good on her promise to disappear, but only for a short time so he would understand she was dead serious.

Most of all, she wanted him to personally experience what it was like to shoulder most of the household and familial responsibilities. She pondered about what responsibility he shared in caring for their children. The answer was that he spent very little time with the children because he was in school most of the time. When he was at home, he required her to have a babysitter for the children if she had to go to the store, or run other errands.

Next, she thought about what her hubby admitted when she kept making inquiries about why it was taking him so long to earn his MBA. In a tirade one day, he growled that he would usually drop some classes, and go to school every day even when he had no classes on a particular day.

Claire Marie finally realized that she had made things too easy for Robert by accepting almost all responsibility for rearing their little ones. She earned the money; kept their home clean; did the cooking; did the laundry; did the shopping; and did the yard work. She ran the kids around like a chauffeur. She edited and typed Robert's schoolwork. She attended family functions with the children, but without Robert. The only task he had was paying the bills — with the money she earned.

She thought about the kind of relationship she and her spouse had with all of the time he spent "away." They still made love, and when they did, she felt more secure, but their life together was surrounded by the circumstances of his education. Nothing was permitted to interfere with his schooling in any way.

Finally, she decided that it would be best to have a frank discussion with Robert to sort out what was real and what was not. Their discussion would have to be without the children or anyone else present, because it would be better with no interruptions. Depending upon how the talk went, she would not disappear until she found out what his intentions were. Perhaps she would not need to disappear. Because she did not want their discussion to turn into an argument, she decided that it would be best to go to a neutral location to talk where neither of them would feel vulnerable.

To this end, she chose a restaurant at which both she and Robert had enjoyed dining in the past. The place's booths were cozy, the noise level was high enough so no one would overhear their conversation, and the food was good and inexpensive. Surprisingly, Robert agreed to go to the restaurant with her without any argument. Claire Marie arranged for the children to spend the evening with their grandparents.

At the restaurant, Claire Marie and Robert made small talk while they were eating. They each had drinks — she had a glass of wine, and he had a screwdriver. When they were on their second drinks, she began the conversation in earnest.

"Do you still enjoy going to school?"

"Of course. Why wouldn't I?"

"Well, it's taking so long for you to finish, I thought you might be ready to give it up."

"My grades are good, especially because you take the time to edit my papers. You're a very good editor. Without you, my grades wouldn't be as good."

"You know, I would like a life like you have to enjoy."

"What's that supposed to mean?"

"Think about it, Robert. You have two responsibilities: You pay the bills and you go to school. You meet and spend time with interesting and exciting people all day. Sometimes, you spend weekends in Chicago working on your thesis. You learn about subjects that I know little about, except what I learn from reading your books. Study groups seem to be a huge part of your life. You have few worries about cooking, cleaning, taking care of our kids, earning money, or even spending much time with us. Honestly, I feel like you're going to dump our kids and me as soon as you get your MBA. We've both seen that happen more than once over these past few years."

"To be honest, Claire Marie, I have considered that."

"And what did you decide — have you already decided?"

"I'm not sure yet what I've decided. You don't even have an undergraduate degree."

"That's true, but it doesn't mean I'm not intelligent and educated."

"There you go again; you just don't understand."

"Oh, but I *do* understand. I understand everything you're doing."

"You're not going to start that again, are you?"

"No, because I can see you're not interested in changing."

"That's being a good girl. Don't start what you can't finish."

"Don't you call me a girl. Let's get out of here."

"Not yet; let's have one more drink."

"Do you still want me to go to Chicago with you a week from Saturday?"

"Yes."

"Well, then I'll need to make arrangements for a sitter."

"Go ahead and do it. You know I still need your help on my Master's thesis."

"Really? Why me? Why don't you ask your *friend*?"

"Don't be stupid. None of my friends are typists. Don't start that bullshit again."

"I should call your *friend* and ask her if she wants to work on your thesis."

"Time to go. C'mon. Don't sit there like a dodo. Our conversation is done. By the way, I really pity you."

"You pity me? Don't you know that 'pity was meant to be a spur that drives joy to help misery.'"?[2]

"No more bullshit. Move it. I need to pay the check so we can get out of here and go home."

---

[2] C., S. Lewis, *The Great Divorce.*

With that, they left the restaurant, and she made plans for the Chicago trip — and finalized her *plan* for the trip.

5

THE PLAN

On the morning of the appointed day, a cold, fall Saturday, Claire Marie and Robert took the kids to their grandparents' home, then began their drive to Chicago. Claire Marie made small talk all the way. So did Robert. He failed to sense her energy or her anxiety. Her heart was pounding so hard that she was sure he might hear it. She acted calm on the outside because she didn't want anything or anyone to discover and foil her plan.

When they arrived in Chicago, but before they reached the university, she abruptly jumped out of the car in the middle of traffic on State Street near Marshall Field's, yelling, "Now it's *your* turn to have fun!" Before Robert could react, Claire Marie sprinted to the sidewalk, blended into a stream of people, and vanished. He was shocked, but behind the wheel of the car, there was nothing he could do.

Walking into Marshall Field's, Claire Marie immediately went up to a pay phone. Taking a deep breath, she dialed the phone number of Robert's "friend."

"Hello?" answered a woman's voice after a couple of rings.

"This is your lover's wife. Don't talk. Just listen. If you don't do what I ask, I will come to your home and tell your husband everything."

"What?"

"Shut up and listen! You get your ass to the Loop, and meet me outside the elevator at the Walnut Room at Marshall Field's. Be here in thirty minutes. Don't bother calling Robert, my *husband*, because he's not home. I know exactly who you are, so I will approach you when you get here. Do you understand what I'm telling you?"

"But..."

"No 'buts.' I'm not kidding. Be here in thirty minutes, or your husband — is he your second or your third, by the way? — will learn everything about your lover. Oh, by the way, do you wear *my* diamond earrings in front of your husband?"

Slamming the receiver on the phone, Claire Marie checked her watch, and then to relax a bit began looking at items for sale.

Twenty-five minutes later, she was standing outside the Walnut Room. She planted both feet squarely on the floor about two feet apart, and assumed a position of power with each hand locked over the opposite elbow and her arms over her breasts. Moments later, she saw Robert's "friend." Feigning confidence, but trembling inside, she sauntered over to the woman.

"I'm Robert's wife."

"What?"

"I'm Robert's wife. Now, walk with me. We are going to walk towards Wieboldts. Just walk. We are going to talk about your "friendship" with my husband while we walk."

"But…you're so…*attractive*," blurted Robert's paramour in surprise.

"Well, thank you," replied Claire Marie icily. "Did you think I was a dog or something?" Looking Robert's "friend" over, Claire Marie continued, "Hell, I'm better looking than you are, and smarter, too. But I must admit that you are, shall I say, his type: Dark hair, dark eyes — like me. But this is the first time he's picked a Spanish girl. By the way, I'm a little French girl."

"You mean, I'm not his first?" responded the woman, again in surprise.

"No. Hell, no. But what you need to know is that he always comes back to me. Not like you, who sleeps around and then changes husbands like I change diapers. Oh yes,

I've done my research on you. In a way, you should thank me for giving you all of this information. After all, I'd so hate to see him break your 'wittow' heart! Oh, and by the way: Today, I left Robert with all five of our kids, all of the bills, all of his schoolwork — and with his Master's thesis to complete by himself, to boot. I guess you know the drill. He has no money, no job. I've been his sole support. So now he'll be dropping out of school to take care of his financial affairs — and, of course, to take care of **his five kids**!"

"You-you can't be serious!" stammered the woman.

"Oh, I'm serious all right. Dead serious. Call Robert later. See what he has to say about me leaving. He has no idea where I am. Are you processing this — *Whore*? You need to break up with him, give him back **my** diamond earrings, and get a real life. You need to do this on Monday when you see him at school — or, sure as shooting, your husband and I will have a very **long** talk in **your** home. I have love notes, hidden in a safe place, of course, that you wrote to Robert. How did I get them? Why, I took from his locker, that's how. And, count on it — unless you do everything that I say, I **will** show all of them to your hubby. Oh, and I almost forgot to show you these!" Claire Marie reached into her purse and removed three objects. "**Your**
40

gloves and hat, which somehow ended up in **my** hubby's locker. I suppose you have some perfectly logical excuse as to how they got there. Maybe your husband would be interested in hearing that excuse."

At this, Claire Marie's eyes narrowed and she stared daggers at her husband's "friend." "You tell Robert anything you want. Just be sure to END it by Monday."

"Give me those!" protested the woman, reaching for her gloves and hat.

"Don't you **dare** try to take them, or I'll make one helluva scene! You have until Monday night to take care of business. Oh, and as Robert may or may not have told you: I **always** do what I say I will do." Finished, Claire Marie abruptly turned her back on the woman, who stood there visibly shaken, and strode angrily away.

Two days later, Monday, turned out to be a bad day all around for Robert. That night after school, he picked up the kids from the sitter — but his beautiful, talented, little French wife was still not at home, was nowhere to be found. He had no idea where she was. He hadn't told anyone about how she had jumped out of the car and ran off. Instead, to keep up appearances, he put up a front, acting as though she was still at home, or at work, even when he picked up the kids from their grandparents' home.

If Claire Marie's disappearance wasn't enough, he also tried in vain to figure out why his "friend" had abruptly broken up with him totally out of the blue that morning; and why, in so doing, she had also returned the beautiful diamond earrings.

He muttered to himself, "What in hell am I going to do with these earrings? Where in hell is my wife? Just who does she think she is?"

At the same time, he wondered just how long she expected him to take care of everything. And then his unfinished thesis popped into his mind. *How am I going to get it done now?*

As the evening continued, he came to take Claire Marie's threat to leave seriously. He had called her work place earlier in the day to see if she might be there, but the receptionist had told him that Claire Marie had applied for and taken a leave of absence. Because he didn't want to disclose that she had disappeared, he said to the receptionist, "Oh yeah. That's right. I guess I just plain forgot for a minute there. I just had a quick question to ask her." Although he didn't reveal anything, in his heart he knew he had sounded stupid.

Yes, that Monday had been a bad day all around for Robert; and, as the week wore on, things got even worse.

On Tuesday, Wednesday and Thursday, he continued the charade. He wondered how his wife did everything with such a cheerful face. The house no longer had its spotless look. The laundry needed to be done, and so did the dishes. By the time the kids asked him to read to them before bedtime, he was dead-tired.

The kids weren't upset about their mother's absence. They explained innocently to their daddy that mommy was looking for a new job that would pay more money. Further, they explained that mommy had told them, "More money is better for everybody."

Robert fretted and worried about the upcoming weekend because he knew that the kids' grandparents might stop over to visit. How would he explain to them his wife's absence?

As of Friday morning, Claire Marie was still gone. By that evening, after the kids were in bed and the house was quiet, he was finally forced to admit to himself that she had clearly made her point.

Sitting in his favorite chair in the living room, with only a night light casting feeble light in the room and eerie shadows on the walls, he lost control of his emotions. He thought about what he had done not only to Claire Marie, but to his whole family. He began weeping, tears streaming

43

from his eyes, his face buried in his hands. He forced himself to cry quietly, as he didn't want to wake the kids and have them see him in his sorry state. The salt from his tears hurt his lip, which he had bitten and cut in trying to stifle his crying. *What am I supposed to do about this mess I've created?* he wondered in despair. He also wondered what had happened to his demons of self-justification, which had vanished in the wake of his wife's absence. Eventually, his heart heavy, he fell asleep in his chair.

Saturday, at 4:30 in the morning, he awoke with a start when he heard the doorbell ring. He went to the door and peeked through the peephole. It was Claire Marie. He unlocked the door as fast as he could. He flung the door wide open and reached for her, but she backed away a little.

"I'm here to talk about some important issues," she stated in a no-nonsense tone.

"No problem!" he blurted. "Come in! Come in! I'm ready to talk about my stupidity. But let's be quiet; the kids are still asleep."

Taking Robert's hand, Claire Marie led him down the hallway to their bedroom. There, they made passionate love.

When they awoke later that morning, they agreed to help each other with the chores that needed doing. They also promised to spend more time with each other, and with their kids. She asked him if his thesis was completed to the point to where she could begin editing and typing it. He asked if, together, they could put in the past the problems with his "friend." Claire Marie agreed that they could. She was somewhat confused by his request, because she couldn't remember everything that had happened during her week away.

When Robert gave her the diamond earrings three weeks later, she awkwardly accepted them.

6

DISORDERLY ORDERLY

Except for ordinary everyday problems, such as her two recurring nightmares and her "Tarantula Delusion," as of 1974, at age thirty-five, Claire Marie believed life was good. She prided herself on the way she was able to juggle her work life, her home life, and, of course, manage her nightmares and "The Tarantula Delusion." She took everything in stride, and believed that her life would continue on in the same positive manner without any other huge challenges. She believed she had her life under control.

By now her eldest son was in his first year of high school, two of the children were in junior high, and the youngest two were in elementary school. In addition, both she and Robert had very good federal civil service jobs. Despite her not having a college degree, she earned only a little less than Robert did, even with his MBA. They rode to and from work together, but worked in different federal agencies.

Unfortunately, it was when she was thirty-five that Claire Marie's idyllic house of cards began to tumble down.

The major cause of this was that her sister Charlene, or Char as she was called, was institutionalized in a mental ward at one of the local hospitals. The circumstances that had brought this about began when Char started acting out and becoming weirder by the day. Moreover, her eyesight without corrective lenses was very poor; and she then began driving without her glasses and bragging about it. At this point her husband, as well as her immediate and extended families, knew something was definitely wrong. The most telling indication came about when Charlene ran naked outside in her neighborhood. She also threatened to kill herself or anyone who got in her way.

Her siblings and her husband managed to convince her to consult with her doctor. While her physician succeeded in talking her into entering the hospital for a mental evaluation, she checked herself out after only the second day. The family then took stronger action, going to court to have her committed to the mental ward out of fear that she would harm either herself or someone else. Over time, little progress was made between Char and her physician. Mostly she just stared into space and was barely communicative. When she did offer any kind of response, it was in a negative vein.

For some reason, one of the hospital orderlies took particular pleasure in being overly strict when he worked with her. One day, after she had been institutionalized in the ward for a month, Char had been exceptionally uncooperative. In response, the orderly confined her to a solitary room, and restrained her to the bed by tying her wrists and her feet to the bed posts. The orderly then instructed her to call out when she needed anything.

Eventually, Char called the orderly because she needed to use the toilet. No response, from the orderly or anyone else. Soon, she was yelling to anyone who might be listening that she needed to use the bathroom; still, no one answered her cries for help. Then she began screaming and thrashing about; but still no one responded, and her voice grew increasingly hoarse from screaming. She begged repeatedly for help because she didn't want to wet herself. But no matter how long and hard she screamed and yelled and begged, no one came to her aid.

Finally, unable to help it, she wet herself. This exasperated her even more, driving her to begin trying to free herself so she could clean up. Working at her restraints for more than three hours, she was finally able to work one of her hands free. Then she freed her other hand. Finally, she worked both her feet free. Rising from the bed, she went to the door, which had a little glass window in it. Grabbing her shoe, she pounded on the window with her shoe until the glass broke.

Hearing the sound of the breaking glass, the orderly responded. Looking insider Char's room, he saw that she was free of her restraints. When he flung open the door and tried to grab and restrain her, she hit him with the powerful straight right punch of a crazy woman, and broke his nose.

Notified about the ruckus, Char's husband was asked to go to the hospital immediately. He telephoned Robert, and together they went to the hospital.

By the time they reached the mental ward, everyone was talking about what Char had done to the orderly. When Char's husband and Robert learned what had happened to her — how she had been tied to her bed and denied help to go to the bathroom despite her hours of desperate pleading — they immediately filed a written and signed complaint with the hospital administrator. In the complaint, they stated that it was totally unreasonable for anyone tied to a bed to have to scream and beg to go to the bathroom for more than three hours. In the report, it was clearly stated that the orderly was more out of order than was Charlene.

They wrote that until the window was broken, no attempt had been made by any hospital personnel to check on her status for more than three hours. In addition, they demanded that a background investigation on the orderly be conducted, based upon his having acted crazier than Charlene on more than one occasion when he had been overly strict with her.

Char's husband and Robert were informed that it would take at least two weeks to conduct a full investigation into the matter. Robert demanded a written response from the hospital administrator; and Robert and Char's husband asked if it was the hospital's standard protocol or practice to restrain and lock up patients who were simply uncooperative, and then leave them unattended for hours.

All the while, other patients, nurses, and orderlies continued talking about the event; and it quickly became common knowledge throughout the ward.

During the intervening two weeks, visits by family members did little to contribute to Charlene's wellbeing. The family also gathered more than once to discuss Char's illness. No one seemed to be able to figure out a cause for her break with reality.

The mystery of Char's illness began to haunt Claire Marie. Moreover, Char began occupying more and more of Claire Marie's thoughts. Over time, Claire Marie began to experience the intuitive sense that, somehow, there was a message, a warning, for her in Char's illness — as though Char's predicament was trying to reveal something to her.

Then one night it happened — another recurrence of her horrific "Purple Mountain Nightmare," which shook her to the very core of her being. Awakening with a start, she found herself wringing wet, feeling nauseated, and shaking all over. And it was then that Claire Marie's intuition told her with stark clarity that her little sister Char had been molested by their grandfather, Yellow Fingers, as well. Claire Marie also knew that **now** she would have to reveal her secret — reveal "The Secret" — to someone. If she failed to do so, she believed, her sister would never get well.

With Charlene still in the hospital, and still not making progress, Claire Marie frantically attempted to get what she knew about "The Secret" from her brain to her mouth. Initially unable to utter to other people the words that would reveal "The Secret," Claire Marie began practicing the words whenever she was alone. When the words ultimately reached her mouth, she could only utter them as almost unintelligible whispers. After three weeks of practice, her whispers finally became softly spoken words. Still, she could not speak the necessary words loudly and clearly.

She worked hard at it for another week, and grew increasingly frantic over her inability to articulate "The Secret" to anyone else. All the while loomed her burgeoning worry that Char would be locked up in a mental ward forever.

Finally, one evening, on the drive home from work with Robert, through sheer force of will, Claire Marie said, in a trembling voice, "Robert. I…I think there's a strong possibility that Char was molested when she was a little girl by our grandfather."

In response, Robert said, "If this is a joke, I'm waiting for the punch line."

"This is no joke." Claire Marie took a deep breath, and continued. "I was molested by our grandfather. So I'm guessing that Char was as well, and that this is what's caused Char's mental problems."

Hearing this shocking revelation caused Robert to lose his concentration, and the car swerved into the next lane, narrowly missing another car. "Next time you have something like this to tell me, please don't do it while I'm driving! But come on, now. This really is a joke, isn't it?"

"No, Robert. I told you — it's not a joke. Someone needs to talk to Charlene, and to her doctor."

"Do you want to be the one to do it, Claire Marie?"

"I can't. It's taken me weeks just to be able to say this much."

"Are you all right?"

"I think so, yes. I thought I had put all of this behind me a long time ago until Char got sick; and then it all came rushing back with the fury of a demon."

That evening, they both went to see Charlene. Char was being unresponsive as usual, so Robert bent down close to her ear, and whispered faintly: "Is all of this because of what your grandfather did to you?"

Slowly, Charlene turned to look at Robert. For a few moments, she gazed at him without saying a word. And then, quietly, she said, "Boy, Robert, you are smart."

Shortly thereafter, Robert had a consultation with Charlene's psychiatrist, and revealed what Claire Marie had told him about Yellow Fingers' acts of molestation. In addition, Charlene's husband received permission to move her to a different hospital. This was important, because another court date was coming up, and no one in the family wanted Char to become upset by the disorderly orderly. Robert also provided information to Charlene's physician about the complaint the family had filed.

An additional appointment was scheduled for Charlene's sisters to meet with the psychiatrist at the hospital. Next, Robert called the rest of the siblings and their spouses, and he called Claire Marie's father to set up a family meeting about this most important issue.

At the family meeting, with the siblings and their spouses present, Claire Marie's father listened intently to each of the girls' stories. Absolute silence reigned until they finished with their stories. At that point, he began to weep openly, crying and trembling so hard that he could scarcely speak.

He whimpered, "Your mother and I didn't know what to do when we caught Pa! We told him to stop, and we thought that he had. Each time we caught him, we thought he would stop. Even when we caught him with one of you and one of the neighbor's girls, we thought we were making him stop. Speaking for your mother and myself, we had no idea whatsoever how sinister his actions were, or how terribly he damaged our entire family. We did what we thought was right. Whom could we have told, and who would have believed us? It haunted your mother until the day she died. I never wanted to be like Pa. I was so afraid of becoming like him that I was afraid to hug my own children. He violated innocent babies. My own father's actions have harmed everyone. Everyone!"

When the four sisters met with the psychiatrist in the hospital, all except the youngest admitted to knowing their grandfather had molested them. The youngest wasn't trying to hide anything; she simply had no recollection of being molested by their grandfather, and was shocked to learn of her sisters' ordeals. She reasoned that because their grandfather was already on his deathbed when she was a little girl, he thus had no opportunity to molest her.

The two older sisters were somewhat reticent, and so didn't disclose the fact that they both experienced nightmares comparable to Claire Marie's. Rather, they assured the psychiatrist that they no longer experienced any problems stemming from the molestations; and, furthermore, that they had developed coping mechanisms on their own. The two middle sisters, including Charlene, had been molested for shorter time periods than Claire Marie. The second eldest sister, Evelyn, shared her recollections.

As a toddler, Evelyn had been very quiet, but had experienced so many horrific nightmares that her parents accurately deduced what was wrong, what Yellow Fingers had done to her, and took her to the family doctor. After examining and talking with the little one, the physician concluded that the reason she was unable to voice her fears or experiences was that she had not yet learned to talk when the molestations had occurred. The physician's advice had been to keep her away from her grandfather, and to continue to watch for any additional problems that might surface as a result of the nightmares. He had suggested that the parents answer questions about the nightmares as truthfully and honestly as possible as soon as Evelyn learned to speak about and question the nightmares.

Evelyn reported that when she was about five or six, she had a horrible nightmare, and asked her mother about it. Her mother explained that it was not only a bad dream, but that it had actually happened. Immediately, however, she had reassured the little girl that she was safe now and she didn't need to be afraid anymore. Evelyn then remembered crying in her mother's arms, and how her mother had comforted her the whole rest of the night.

After the sixth session, the psychiatrist concluded that Claire Marie and Evelyn were both in good health mentally and that both understood fully what had happened to them. He expressed his belief that they would be able to carry on their lives successfully. They were then invited to make individual appointments immediately if they experienced any difficulties in the future.

The psychiatrist explained to each of the four sisters that one peril might still exist; he called it Post-Traumatic Stress Disorder, PTSD for short. He revealed that the medical community was learning much about PTSD due to the combat experiences of Viet Nam war veterans during that war. He explained that often a noise, or a scent, or even a picture could make a person feel like he or she was experiencing past events as if they were occurring for the very first time. He called this phenomenon a "Flashback."

The psychiatrist informed Charlene that he wanted her to undergo additional sessions with him in the hospital setting before she went before the judge during the upcoming court hearing.

Before Char completed her sessions with the psychiatrist, her former hospital's investigation of the disorderly orderly and his methods was completed. The investigation, precipitated by the family's written complaint, revealed that a complete background check of the orderly's employment history, a process required under hospital policy for all potential new hires, had not been conducted. The investigation further disclosed that the disorderly orderly had escaped from a mental institution in a neighboring state, and had then managed to get hired at the hospital in which Charlene had been initially committed.

The hospital administrator stated that he had summarily discharged the orderly the day the investigation concluded, based upon his history as a mental patient. Furthermore, the disorderly orderly was consequently readmitted to the mental hospital from which he had escaped. At first, the hospital administrator refused to provide a written copy of the report to the family; instead, he expected them to accept his explanation. However, the family immediately threatened legal action, which convinced the administrator to provide limited access to a copy of the report maintained in the hospital's confidential records. This *quid pro quo* required the family to keep the information in the report confidential.

Following the group psychiatric sessions with her sisters, and as a result of her continued psychiatric sessions in the hospital, Charlene began showing noticeable improvement. Her progress was so positive that it became increasingly clear that the family would soon be able to go back to court to try and have her institutionalization reversed. The court hearing was scheduled to take place six weeks after the final psychiatric group meeting with all of the sisters.

On the day of the hearing, prior to the scheduled time, Robert asked one of the bailiffs if family members would be able to speak to the judge in chambers before they met officially. Unexpectedly, the judge allotted the family fifteen minutes before the hearing. During their brief meeting with the judge, Robert led the discussion, explaining confidentially what had happened to Charlene at the hands of the mentally ill orderly. Other family members then started to explain the root of Charlene's initial institutionalization, but the judge stopped them, advising them to save their testimony until court was in session. The family then explained their confidentiality requirement with the hospital, but provided the judge with the orderly's name.

Amazingly, it turned out that the judge personally knew the administrator of the hospital where Charlene had initially been committed. Much to everyone's surprise, the judge immediately grabbed the telephone and called the administrator. Stating that he had received some confidential information about an incident that needed verification, he told the administrator over the phone, in front of the family, that he would keep the information confidential. After he concluded his telephone conversation, the judge called the situation a "goddamned mess," and then stated, "I'll see you in court in ten minutes."

After listening to the statements and testimony of several of the family members, and after reading the psychiatrist's report, he ruled that Charlene could be released from the hospital. For some reason, however, he was angry with the family for having "used the system," as he termed it, to advance their cause. On the one hand, he admonished the family for having done so. But he also stated that he understood why they had. He concluded the proceedings by stating forcefully, "No more similar shenanigans will be allowed in my courtroom. Go home."

7

DEPUTY BADGE

After revealing "The Secret" to Robert, Claire Marie believed that she would feel differently, that she would be less afraid, and that the nightmares would cease. What had changed to make her feel this way was the fact that her husband, her father, and her siblings now all knew as much as she did about what had happened to her at the hands of her grandfather when she was a child.

Furthermore, she now believed with conviction that she was, indeed, The Little Girl In The Blue Dress in her nightmare. She still lacked a clear vision of why she could not remember everything that had happened to her. Her memory always went blank when Yellow Fingers moved his rough hand to her panties. Every time she awoke following "The Purple Mountain Nightmare," she always found herself choking and having difficulty breathing. However, she would awaken before she could see what had happened to cause her breathlessness and choking. She didn't want to think about these matters because doing so caused her heart to race, and she would often throw up; but she knew intuitively that she had to know more, no matter how painful or difficult the knowledge would be.

She toyed with the idea of putting all those thoughts and feelings away forever, but at the same time doubted that such was wise or even possible. She thought about the sessions with the psychiatrist and her sisters. Now she understood why her father had always been so distant — he didn't want to become like his own father. Still, she couldn't understand why she had blank spots in her memory, or why the nightmares wouldn't go away.

Finally she decided to figure out, on her own, what had actually happened to her, and what the blank spots in her nightmares were. She desperately wanted to rid herself of this baggage.

Although the nightmares continued, they came less frequently for a while; but when she awoke, she always still felt just as vulnerable, helpless, sick, and afraid as she had felt in the past. Yet she was unable to figure out what "The Purple Mountain Nightmare" represented. She decided to let her search for answers proceed unfettered. She also determined to open her mind to all memories, no matter how unsavory or unpleasant they would prove to be. Whenever she was alone, she would say out loud, "I don't need to hide from my past. I am a grown woman, and I can

work this out. I need to know about the Purple Mountain."
When she prayed at night, she asked God to allow all of her memories to come flooding back. The black tarantulas still descended from the ceiling; and she would run her hands through them, knowing they were not there, were not real.

One day, when her eldest daughter was a junior in high school, she asked her mother out of the blue, after school, if her girlfriend Becky could stay overnight. It was a school night, and Claire Marie reminded her daughter of this fact.

"Mom, I know it's a school night, but Becky's mom said it would be okay."

"Why would her mom give Becky permission to stay at our home on a school night?"

"Her mom also said that if it was all right with you and dad, she could stay here for a while, and her brothers would bring her bedroom furniture over here."

"What am I missing in this conversation?"

"Becky got stuck in her bedroom window last night."

"What?!"

"Well...I don't know how to say it, Mom, so I'll just say it. Her dad has been — you know — molesting her, and when she tried to climb out through her window to get

65

away, she got stuck. It's a real little window, Mom. Becky's mother is afraid of her dad. Becky told me he's mean, and sometimes he hurts her mom. You've met her mom; she's just a tiny woman."

"How long has her mother known?"

"I don't know, but Becky can't take it anymore."

"Did Becky or her mother call the police? What about counseling for Becky?"

"No, but her mom's afraid of her dad and of what people would say. They don't want people to know."

"She can stay the night, and we'll talk more tomorrow after school."

As it turned out, Becky lived with Claire Marie and her family for more than two years. She went home to visit her mother only at times when her father was away from home. After Becky's father suffered a stroke, which disabled him to the extent that he could no longer violate his lovely daughter, Becky moved back home.

Her father, confined to a wheel chair, required special care. Both Becky and Claire Marie wished secretly that the stroke had been fatal, and both prayed secretly that he would die soon. They wondered why God had permitted such an evil man to live. But they both also thanked God for having rendered him an invalid.

During the period when Becky lived with Claire Marie and her family, "The Purple Mountain Nightmare" troubled and frightened Claire Marie more frequently than it had in years. Still, it always ended the same way — with her not knowing everything that had happened.

The night Claire Marie learned that Becky would be moving back home, "The Purple Mountain Nightmare" assaulted her yet again. This time, however, the entire nightmare played out clearly, with no blank spots.

She saw herself lying on Yellow Fingers' kitchen table. She was wearing a blue dress.

"Look at it, isn't it nice and big?" said Yellow Fingers. "You can touch it if you want. Would you like to kiss it? That would make Grandpa very happy. You want to make Grandpa happy, don't you?"

"No! I don't want to! I'm afraid!"

"If you kiss it I'll give you my Deputy Badge."

"I don't want your badge!"

"C'mon now, we don't have much time. Your mother and father will be back soon. Look — the badge is so nice and shiny, and you can be a deputy if I give it to you."

"No! I'm too little to be a deputy! I don't want your dumb old badge!"

"You listen to me, you little brat! You'll get in big trouble if you don't make me happy! You better kiss it now! You'll like it. I promise."

"No!"

"Ma! Get in here! I know you're hiding in the bedroom and I know you can hear me! I need your help! Now!"

From the bedroom, Ma said, "Please, Pa! Don't make me do it again!"

"You'll do as I say, or you know what will happen to you! Think about the last time you refused. I can punish you again."

A moment later, entering the kitchen fearfully, Ma stepped hesitantly up to the table.

"Hold her still, Ma! God damn it! Pinch her nose!"

Awakening with a start, Claire Marie could feel her heart pounding furiously and she was drenched in perspiration. Now, at long last, with crystal clarity, she knew exactly what had happened to her as a little girl, but she could not believe it for several minutes. She wanted to lie still, but her entire body was shaking uncontrollably.

Letting the horrible truth sink into her mind, she slowly and silently slipped out of bed without awakening Robert. Padding softly into the bathroom, she knelt in front

68

of the toilet and vomited into the bowl. After washing her face and rinsing her mouth, she buried her face in the fluffy bath towels hanging from the wall and let her tears flow freely.

8

WHITE TARANTULAS

After having finally experienced the entire "Purple Mountain Nightmare" in all its ugly detail, Claire Marie was certain that she would feel dramatically different. But she didn't. Nothing changed in the way she walked, talked, looked, thought, or acted.

However, very significant changes did occur that changed her life forever. First, she never experienced "The Purple Mountain Nightmare" or "The Little Girl In The Blue Dress Nightmare" ever again.

Then, one night about two weeks later, she went to bed as usual. After she had been asleep for about two and a half hours, she awoke with a start. She opened her eyes, and looked up at the ceiling. And there it was again: "The Tarantula Delusion." *Or was it?* she asked herself. Rubbing her eyes, she looked up again. At first glance, the Delusion was the same as she had seen it almost every night for years. Hanging from the ceiling were fifteen or twenty huge furry tarantulas, suspended from the ceiling by long cords of different lengths. There were little tarantulas hanging at different levels from the huge ones. Only this time there was one major difference: All of the tarantulas were *white*. Knowing, as always, that they weren't actually there, Claire Marie lifted her hand as usual to try and touch them. Her hand touched nothing as she waved it through the tarantulas. Then the entire Delusion, and with it all of the tarantulas, disappeared before her very eyes. However, unlike as in the past, no wave of nausea rippled through her body. No panicky feeling shook her. She didn't feel sick, nor was she shaking. Wondering what this all meant, she just laid there awake.

"The Tarantula Delusion" never returned. She was elated over its departure, but was puzzled as to why it had just disappeared — and why it had disappeared, for good as it turned out, after the one occurrence in which all of the tarantulas had been white.

Like almost everything else connected with Yellow Fingers, Claire Marie thought hard about and analyzed it. She finally came to understand that the tarantulas turning white was a sign that she had at last been freed of her fear associated with her grandfather.

Claire Marie also knew that she could now close that part of her life. While she knew that her molestation at the hands of Yellow Fingers would always be a part of her past life, she now realized that she no longer needed to fear her past, nor allow it frighten her, nor make her sick.

And it was with that realization that Claire Marie permitted the frightened and terrified Little Girl In The Blue Dress, with holes in her memory, to depart from her psyche.

After a year had passed, life for Claire Marie, at age thirty-six, was good. Everything she had worked for and towards was on a positive track. She rarely felt the need to talk about her experiences with anyone, including Robert, any longer. She accepted the baggage of her past as being a part of who she was; and she was especially proud of herself for having conquered and overcome a pedophile's damage to her psyche.

She genuinely liked herself, and appreciated everything she had worked so hard to earn, including her previously suppressed memories. On rare occasions, she experienced flashbacks, but each time she sorted things out and refused to submit to fear. Through her strength of will, with every fiber of her being, she steadfastly refused to allow her past to overpower her present.

Thirty-four years later, in 1999, when Claire Marie was sixty years old, the phone rang on a quiet evening. She picked up the receiver and answered...

9

TELEPHONE CALLS

"Hello?"

"Is that you, Claire Marie?"

"Yes, who is this?"

"It's Betty, your cousin. Remember me?"

"Of course I do, Betty. How are you?"

"Well...I'm having some problems, and I hope I can talk with you about them."

"Sure. What's going on?"

"Did you know that our grandfather molested me?"

Claire Marie sighed deeply. "I didn't know for sure how many of us were violated. He molested me and two of my three sisters."

"Recently, my husband and I had to start taking our son to counseling because he's becoming unmanageable. He's changed from being a sweet little boy to a stranger who lies all the time. He stares into space. I don't know for sure, but I think he's also dabbling in drugs! From the counseling it's finally come out that he was being molested by our parish priest! Our parish priest! He was afraid to tell us because the priest told him he was supposed to keep it a secret. He was also afraid that we wouldn't believe him if he told us. And here we sent him to Catholic school to protect him from such things. Until this emerged in the counseling, I had never told anyone about what happened to me. I'm so worked up about this and so worried about my son. Claire Marie, I've cried and cried until I have no more tears."

"Oh, God!" gasped Claire Marie in horror. "Betty, I don't have any specific answers for you. But it sounds like you're doing everything you should be doing, and everything I would do. My best advice is to keep trying and trying until you find something that helps. What happened to the priest?"

"The archdiocese transferred him to a different state, but they won't tell us where. My husband and I don't even know if he's still in the same archdiocese. But we do know that the priest wasn't even disciplined. They just kept on denying that he did anything to our son. If he was anything like our grandfather, you know that he violated more than one child. I know our son would never lie about something like this."

"Betty, get yourself a good lawyer. This is preposterous. If only we lived closer to one another. If I could hug you right now, I would."

76

"Is it all right if I call you from time to time to talk?"

"Of course, Betty. I'll do anything I can to help. Our grandfather hurt so many people, and not only those he molested. He was like a polluted pebble dropped into a puddle. The waves from that foul pebble just keep moving out until they reach the edges of the puddle and contaminate everything."

"Claire Marie, I'm so frightened for my son! I don't even believe in God anymore! Well...thanks for talking with me. At least I feel a little relief knowing that you understand."

After that evening, Claire Marie and Betty talked by phone frequently. Usually, Betty would call in an agitated state, and reveal how nothing seemed to be helping her son. Betty and her husband tried individual counseling, group counseling, and hypnosis, but these measures barely made any inroads at all into their son's troubled mind.

Moreover, their lawyer was getting nowhere fast with the priest's parish or the archdiocese.

Claire Marie always listened compassionately, offered words of comfort from her heart, and at times put forth suggestions she thought might be helpful.

In 2002, Betty called Claire Marie on a Saturday morning.

"Hello?"

"This is Betty."

"Hi, Betty. What's up?"

"Everything is over." Her voice was flat. Lifeless.

"What do you mean, 'over'?" asked Claire Marie. Suddenly she heard Betty dissolve into sobbing and unintelligible words. "Slow down, Betty! I'm here for you! What's wrong?"

"My...My beautiful son is gone forever. He...He...*killed* himself!" choked Betty. "He left a note. He just couldn't sort it all out. I tried, Claire Marie. My husband tried. The doctors tried." In between sobs Betty continued, "Maybe we didn't try hard enough. His note said that he loved us. The last line he wrote was, 'I'm sorry, please forgive me.' God, Claire Marie!"

"It's not your fault, Betty. It's not your son's fault. It's not your husband's fault. It's that goddamn priest's fault! He's the one who's guilty — along with anyone else who covered it up. I hope they all burn in hell!"

"Will you come to the fu...funeral?"

"You know I will, Betty."

As soon as Claire Marie hung up the phone, she could feel all of the old wounds resurfacing. She went into the bathroom and buried her face in the fluffy towels. She cried until she had no more tears left.

Splashing cold water on her face, she felt the urge to be let her mind wander to her "Safe Place," as she had done in the face of Yellow Fingers' onslaughts. It would be so easy to run away from Betty's son's death that way. She had not gone to the "Safe Place" in many, many years. She was afraid and shaking. She felt sick, nauseous, as she wondered, *Why do some people perpetrate such horrors on those around them?* Her mind began to drift away to her "Safe Place." But with all her force of will, she was able to fight off her mind's urge to run away.

Instead, she let go of the towels, stood up straight, and walked out of the bathroom. Picking up her cell phone she dialed Robert, who was at the gym working out. When he answered, she said, "Robert, I have some very bad news."

After Claire Marie informed Robert of the tragedy, she sat down at her personal computer and began composing a letter to her bishop.

She wrote the following:

For many years, pedophilia has been bubbling up in the Roman Catholic Church. Only recently, the cloak of secrecy surrounding this issue has begun to erode. Now the Church has the opportunity to make sweeping changes by cleansing the unholy orders. Failure to work at diligently removing the cause of our collapse in human decency will continue to damage our Church. The faithful will always be there, but we will <u>not</u> be there to provide ongoing support for evil.

Sincerely,
Claire Marie

ABOUT THE AUTHOR

Bruna Slava, the author, lives in the Midwest with her husband and their dog.

CPSIA information can be obtained at www.ICGtesting.com
Printed in the USA
LVOW06s1821111115

462089LV00024B/584/P